Rabbiting On

Kit and Posy hope that these —
Find some favour with The Weasel;
Also Stephen (call him King).
May these pics and poems bring
Joy to Anna J and Sarah,
Who'll be kind enough to share a
Look at then with Caroline
(Pics by Posy, poems mine).
Then there's Becky and her pal,
The boy the bruisers call Big Al.
To them and all the rest who like
With sawn-off walking sticks to strike
A tennis ball a mighty way
On that fine golf-course, Booby's Bay,
We dedicate the book upon
Whose cover you'll read RABBITING ON . . . .

Kit Wright is far too tall and likes poems, beer, cricket
and Posy Simmonds.

Posy Simmonds likes drawing, Kit's jokes, singing in the
bath and wine gums.

Rabbiting On

and Other Poems

by Kit Wright

Illustrations by Posy Simmonds

A Fontana Young Lions Original

First published in Fontana Young Lions 1978
8 Grafton Street, London W1X 3LA
Seventh impression November 1986

Fontana Young Lions is an imprint of
Fontana Paperbacks, part of
the Collins Publishing Group

Made and printed in Great Britain by
William Collins Sons & Co. Ltd, Glasgow

Contents

Rabbiting On

Where did you go?
Oh . . . nowhere much.

What did you see?
Oh . . . rabbits and such.

Rabbits? What else?
Oh . . . a rabbit hutch.

What sort of rabbits?
What sort? Oh . . . small.

What sort of hutch?
Just a hutch, that's all.

But what did it look like?
Like a rabbit hutch.

Well, what was in it?
Small rabbits and such.

I worried about you
While you were gone.

*Why don't you stop
Rabbiting on?*

Me

My Mum is on a diet,
My Dad is on the booze,
My Gran's out playing Bingo
And she was born to lose.

My brother's stripped his motorbike
Although it's bound to rain.
My sister's playing Elton John
Over and over again.

What a dim old family!
What a dreary lot!
Sometimes I think that I'm the only
Superstar they've got.

Whisper Whisper

whisper whisper
whisper whisper
goes my sister
down the phone

whisper whisper
go the beech leaves
breathing in the
wind alone

whisper whisper
whisper whisper
slips the river
on the stone

whisper whisper
go my parents
when they whisper
on their own

I don't mind the
whisper whisper
whisper whisper
it's a tune

sometimes though
I wish the whisper
whisperings would
shut up soon

The Wicked Singers

And have you been out carol singing,
Collecting for the Old Folk's Dinner?

Oh yes indeed, oh yes indeed.

And did you sing all the Christmas numbers,
Every one a winner?

Oh yes indeed, oh yes indeed.

Good King Wenceslas, and Hark
The Herald Angels Sing?

Oh yes indeed, oh yes indeed.

And did you sing them loud and clear
And make the night sky ring?

Oh yes indeed, oh yes indeed.

And did you count up all the money?
Was it quite a lot?

Oh yes indeed, oh yes indeed.

And did you give it all to the Vicar,
Everything you'd got?

Certainly not, certainly not.

My Party

My parents said I could have a party
And that's just what I did.

Dad said, "Who had you thought of inviting?"
I told him. He said, "Well, you'd better start writing,"
And that's just what I did

To:
Phyllis Willis, Horace Morris,
Nancy, Clancy, Bert and Gert Sturt,
Dick and Mick and Nick Crick,
Ron, Don, John,
Dolly, Molly, Polly—
Neil Peel—
And my dear old friend, Dave Dirt.

I wrote, "Come along, I'm having a party,"
And that's just what they did.

They all arrived with huge appetites
As Dad and I were fixing the lights.
I said, "Help yourself to the drinks and bites!"
And that's just what they did,
All of them:

Phyllis Willis, Horace Morris,
Nancy, Clancy, Bert and Gert Sturt,
Dick and Mick and Nick Crick,
Ron, Don, John,
Dolly, Molly, Polly-
Neil Peel—
And my dear old friend, Dave Dirt.

Now, I had a good time and as far as I could tell,
The party seemed to go pretty well—
Yes, that's just what it did.

Then Dad said, "Come on, just for fun,
Let's have a *turn* from everyone!"
And a turn's just what they did,

All of them:

Phyllis Willis, Horace Morris,
Nancy, Clancy, Bert and Gert Sturt,
Dick and Mick and Nick Crick,
Ron, Don, John,
Dolly, Molly, Polly—
Neil Peel—
And my dear old friend, Dave Dirt.

AND THIS IS WHAT THEY DID:

Phyllis and Clancy
And Horace and Nancy
Did a song and dance number
That was really fancy—

Dolly, Molly, Polly,
Ron, Don and John
Performed a play
That went on and on and on—

Gert and Bert Sturt,
Sister and brother,
Did an imitation of
Each other.

(Gert Sturt put on Bert Sturt's shirt
And Bert Sturt put on Gert Sturt's skirt.)

Neil Peel
All on his own
Danced an eightsome reel.

Dick and Mick
And Nicholas Crick
Did a most *ingenious*
Conjuring trick

And my dear old friend, Dave Dirt,
Was terribly sick
All over the flowers.
We cleaned it up.
It took *hours*.

But as Dad said, giving a party's not easy.
You really
Have to
Stick at it.
I agree. And if Dave gives a party
I'm certainly
Going to be
Sick at it.

Doris

There was a young lady called Doris
Who had a twin sister called Chloris,
    One brother called Maurice,
    Another called Norris
And two more called Horace and Boris.

Now Doris was quite fond of Chloris
And she didn't mind Maurice or Norris
    But she hated Horace
    And Horace loathed Boris

And Horace, Boris, Maurice, Norris
and Chloris couldn't take Doris *at
any price at all.*

Give Up Slimming, Mum

My Mum
is short
and plump
and pretty
and I wish
she'd give up
slimming.

So does Dad.

Her cooking's
delicious—
you can't
beat it—
but you really can
hardly bear
to eat it—
the way she sits
with her eyes
brimming,
watching you
polish off
the spuds
and trimmings
while she
has nothing
herself but a small
thin dry
diet biscuit:
that's all.

My Mum
is short
and plump
and pretty
and I wish
she'd give up
slimming.

So does Dad.

She says she
looks as though
someone had
sat on her—
BUT WE LIKE MUM
WITH A BIT
OF FAT ON HER!

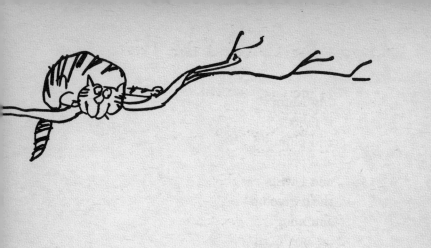

Dad and the Cat and the Tree

This morning a cat got
Stuck in our tree.
Dad said, "Right, just
Leave it to me."

The tree was wobbly,
The tree was tall.
Mum said, "For goodness'
Sake don't fall!"

"Fall?" scoffed Dad,
"A climber like me?
Child's play, this is!
You wait and see."

He got out the ladder
From the garden shed.
It slipped. He landed
In the flower bed.

"Never mind", said Dad,
Brushing the dirt
Off his hair and his face
And his trousers and his shirt,

"We'll try Plan B. Stand
Out of the way!"
Mum said, "Don't fall
Again, O.K.?"

"Fall again?" said Dad.
"Funny joke!"
Then he swung himself up
On a branch. It broke.

Dad landed *wallop*
Back on the deck.
Mum said, "Stop it,
You'll break your neck!"

"Rubbish!" said Dad.
"Now we'll try Plan C.
Easy as winking
To a climber like me!"

Then he climbed up high
On the garden wall.
Guess what?
He *didn't fall*!

He gave a great leap
And he landed flat
In the crook of the tree-trunk—
Right on the cat!

The cat gave a yell
And sprang to the ground,
Pleased as Punch to be
Safe and sound.

So it's smiling and smirking,
Smug as can be,
But poor old Dad's
Still

Stuck
Up
The
Tree!

Grandad

Grandad's dead
And I'm sorry about that.

He'd a huge black overcoat.
He felt proud in it.
You could have hidden
A football crowd in it.
Far too big—
It was a lousy fit
But Grandad didn't
Mind a bit.
He wore it all winter
With a squashed black hat.

Now he's dead
And I'm sorry about that.

He'd got twelve stories.
I'd heard every one of them
Hundreds of times
But that was the fun of them:
You knew what was coming
So you could join in.
He'd got big hands
And brown, grooved skin
And when he laughed
It knocked you flat.

Now he's dead
And I'm sorry about that.

My Dad, Your Dad

My dad's fatter than your dad,
Yes, my dad's fatter than yours:
If he eats any more he won't fit in the house,
He'll have to live out of doors.

Yes, but my dad's balder than your dad,
My dad's balder, O.K.,
He's only got two hairs left on his head
And both are turning grey.

Ah, but my dad's thicker than your dad,
My dad's thicker, all right.
He has to look at his watch to see
If it's noon or the middle of the night.

Yes, but my dad's more boring than your dad.
If he ever starts counting sheep
When he can't get to sleep at night, he finds
It's the sheep that go to sleep.

But my dad doesn't mind your dad.
Mine quite likes yours too.
I suppose they don't always think much of US!
That's true, I suppose, that's true.

Did You Ever!

Did you ever
Meet an old man in a sky-blue overcoat?
Yes? Well, so did I.

Hat on his head,
Hands on his knees,
Beard on his face,
Pipe in his mouth
And a look in his eye
That said:
"I may not be too clever, folks,
But goodness knows, I try!"

You met him and so did I.

Did you ever
Meet an old woman in a sharkskin waistcoat?
Yes? Well, so did I.

    Cap on her head,
    Freckles on her knees,
    Grin on her face,
    Twig in her mouth
    And a look in her eye
    That said:
    "I'm feeling frisky as a two-week kitten,
    Somebody tell me why!"

You met her and so did I.

Did you ever
Meet an old dog in velvet trousers?
Never? Neither did I.

Swaybacks in the Springtime

Two old horses, piebald swaybacks,
Mooching down by the chestnut trees:
Sharing a field in spring, though these
Are the winter days of their lives.

Two old horses, put out to grass here,
Suddenly break, frisk into a run
And their tough manes gleam in the rising sun
In the winter days of their lives.

Sergeant Brown's Parrot

Many policemen wear upon their shoulders
Cunning little radios. To pass away the time
They talk about the traffic to them, listen to the news,
And it helps them to Keep Down Crime.

But Sergeant Brown, he wears upon his shoulder
A tall green parrot as he's walking up and down
And all the parrot says is ''Who's-a-pretty-boy-then?''
''I am,'' says Sergeant Brown.

Sergeant Brown's Parrot's Girl-Friend

Sergeant Brown's parrot's girl-friend
Squawked to herself in a hickory tree:
"They say my parrot boy's no good,
They say he's lousy as can be.
   They put him down
   In every way
   But what I say
Is: Good enough for Sergeant Brown
   Is good enough for me!"

That splendid Sergeant Brown
That strides about the town!

So Sergeant Brown's parrot's girl-friend
Flew till she came where Sergeant Brown,
Her tall green lover on his shoulder,
Was pacing grandly up and down.
  She whispered low
  In her lover's ear:
  "It's me, my dear.
Tell me, truly, who's-a-pretty-girl-then?"
  "I am," said Sergeant Brown.

That frightful Sergeant Brown
That strides about the town!

Sergeant Brown's Parrot and Sir Robert Mark

Sir Robert Mark, Police Commissioner,
Heard of a Sergeant who had dared to position a

Parrot on his shoulder. "A what?" he said.
"PARROT. TALL. GREEN. ALONGSIDE HIS HEAD.

SMART. WELL-SPOKEN. A BIRD OF BREEDING.
PROCEEDS WHEREVER THE SERGEANT'S PROCEEDING."

The report was delivered at a Working Luncheon.
Sir Robert banged his plate with his silver truncheon.

The plate broke in half. No-one dared to laugh.
"Bring this man in!" he roared to his staff.

The Sergeant was working on a dog theft case,
Sitting at his desk with his parrot in place.

"Come on, Brown!" they yelled, "better make it snappy—
Sir Robert Mark wants you and he isn't too happy!"

So off went the Sergeant and the parrot and the rest of them,
Arrived where Sir Robert was scoffing with the best of them.

Sergeant and parrot strolled into the meeting.
Everyone stopped talking. Everyone stopped eating.

Sir Robert looked the pair of them up and down
With a dangerous look in his eye. He said, "Brown,

I've seen some things in the Force, my *word* upon it,
But never once a Sergeant with a shoulder with a bird upon i

Take it off at once, you ridiculous clown!"
"Shut your beak," said Sergeant Brown.

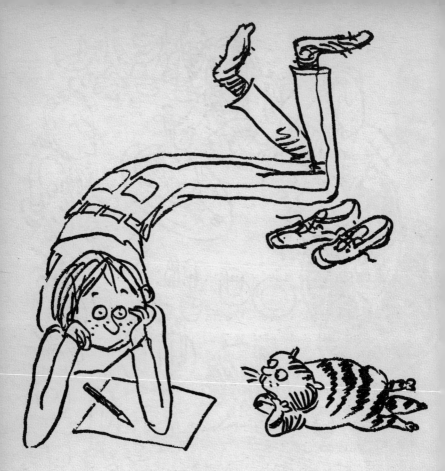

Some Days

I didn't find it interesting,
Listening,
I didn't find it interesting,
Talking,
So I left the house—I went miles and miles—
And I didn't find it interesting,
Walking.

I didn't find it interesting,
Reading,
I didn't find it interesting,
Writing,
So I left the house—I went miles and miles—
And that wasn't terribly
Exciting.

I watched my sister playing
Patience,
But I didn't find it interesting,
Scoring,
So I left the house—I went miles and miles—
And that was *extremely*
Boring.

I didn't find it interesting,
Telly,
There wasn't much on
That night,
So I sat in a chair and I went to sleep,
A dull old day
All right.

Some People

You can't tell some people anything.

I told my friend a secret.
"It dies with me," he said.
Then he dropped dead.

You can't tell some people anything.

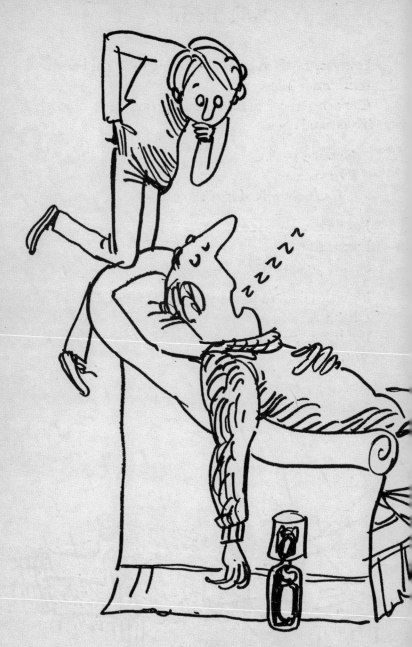

Dad's Beard

Last year my Dad grew a great big thick red beard:
Mum made him.
Can't think how in the world she managed
To persuade him.

Nothing but hair
Everywhere:
Can't say I liked it at all.

But now he's shaved it,
I wonder:
Should he have saved it?

It's odd. Did Dad look better with his beard?
I doubt it.
But he certainly looks pretty weird
Without it.

Nothing but face
All over the place:
Can't say I like it at all.

Uncle Joe's Jalopy

When you're riding in my Uncle Joe's jalopy,
Better hang on tight 'cos the roads are pretty choppy
When you're travelling in that car.

It's a dumpy little jumpy little bumpy little number
And it doesn't pay to sleep and it doesn't pay to slumber
And you'd best not go too far
When you're travelling in that car.

It's got holes in the roof the snow has snowed through,
Holes in the floor you can see the road through,
Holes in the dash the petrol's flowed through—
Pretty scary car!

It's got broken springs—brakes on the blink—
Wheels that wobble—fumes that stink—
And the windscreen's turned as black as ink
So you can't see where you are
When you're travelling in that car:
So you'd best not   go too   far!

But don't you *criticize* that jalopy
Or Uncle Joe will get mighty stroppy
'Cos he really likes that car!

When he's at the wheel of that old bone-shaker
He thinks he's a Grand Prix record-breaker—
He thinks he's a motor star!

When he bangs round corners on two square wheels
Folks on the pavement take to their heels
'Cos they don't feel as safe as Uncle Joe feels
When he's travelling in that car:

And as for me, I can't wait for the day
When the wheels fall off and the roof blows away
And Uncle Joe will just have to say,
"Well, that's the end of that car:
It really can't   go too   far!"

I Don't Like You

If I were the Prime Minister of Britain
And you were a snail
I'd be most careful walking round my garden
Not to disturb your trail.

If I were a snail and you were the Prime Minister
It wouldn't be like that.
You'd tramp around in your expensive boots
And squash me flat.

I Like You

When you're unkind
You don't mean to be.
And when you're kind
You couldn't care less
Whether or not
You're seen to be.

What I like about you
Is how you know what's cooking
In somebody else's mind.
You do the best you can
And you just don't care
Who's looking.

Ghosts

That's right. Sit down and talk to me.
What do you want to talk about?

Ghosts. You were saying that you believe in them.
Yes, they exist, without a doubt.

What, bony white nightmares that rattle and glow?
No, just spirits that come and go.

I've never heard such a load of rubbish.
Never mind, one day you'll know.

What makes you so sure?

I said:
What makes you so sure?

Hey,
Where did you go?

Six White Skeletons

Deep deep down in the sea in the deep sea darkness
where the big fish
flicker and loom
and the weeds are alive
like hair

the hull of the wreck
grates in the sand:
in and out
of its ribs of steel—
only the long eel
moves there.

Down in the engine-room
six white skeletons:

only the long eel
moves there.

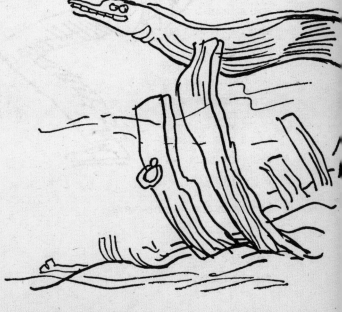

Nutter

The moon's a big white football,
The sun's a pound of butter.
The earth is going round the twist
And I'm a little nutter!

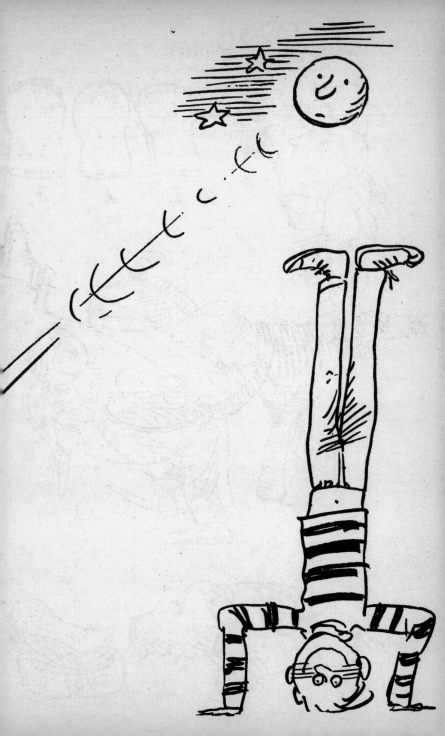

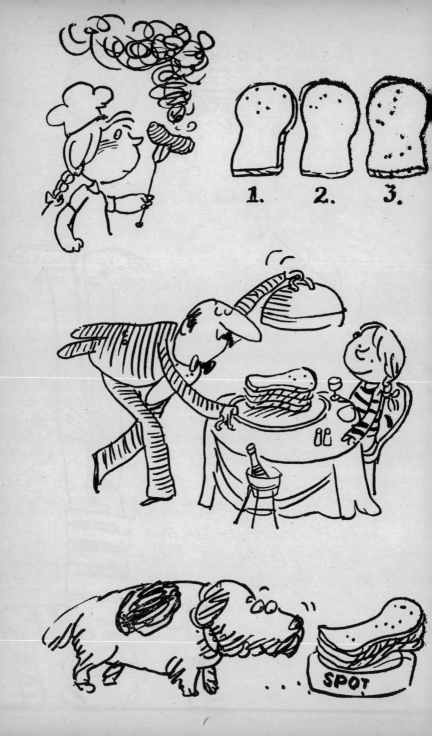

1.   2.   3.

SPOT

If You're No Good at Cooking

If you're no good at cooking,
Can't fry or bake,

Here's something you
Can always make. Take

Three very ordinary
Slices of bread:

Stack the second
On the first one's head.

Stack the third
On top of that.

There! Your three slices
Lying pat.

So what have you got?
A BREAD SANDWICH,

That's what!
Why not?

A Visit to the Aquarium

Watching the conger eel

(a three foot slice of muscle,
a blue blade of steel
that cast a motionless shadow
on the lit glass floor of its cell)

I saw the sudden whiplash ripple
of its whole body
that crashed the plunging water
as it swallowed
and then was still

And I thought of my friend Dave Dirt,
too fast to live, too young to die,
who
sudden as lightning

SWIPED

the Last Cake
at Phyllis Willis's birthday party!

Dave and the conger eel:
neither of them like to leave
anything to chance . . .
or to anyone
else.

Snoozing by the Boozer

All day outside the boozer snores
The boozer-keeper's big brown dog
And carefully each boozer-user
Coming to or from the boozer
Steps around the shaggy snoozer,
   Dumped there like a log.

It chanced a fellow named de Souza
(An American composer)
Once was passing by the boozer
Humming to himself a Blues. A
Dog-enthuser, this de Souza,
So he halted by the boozer.
With his stick he poked the snoozer.
"Big brown dog," he said, "say who's a
   Good boy then?" This shows a

Lack of knowledge of the boozer-
Keeper's dog. It is a bruiser,
   Not a dreamy dozer.

Up it sprang and ate de Souza,
The American composer.
He is dead, the dog-enthuser.

Don't poke dogs outside the boozer.
You are bound to be the loser.

Frankie and Johnny are Useless

Now, Frankie's a nimble showjumper,
Like Princess Anne over the course,
But she jumped the waterjump one day
And that waterjump drowned her horse—

It was her thing
But she did it wrong.

Well, Johnny's a brilliant goalie,
I've not seen a better one yet,
But he let through so many goals one game,
Bust a hole in the back of the net—

It was his thing
But he did it wrong.

Now, Frankie's a dab hand at cooking,
She was cooking the family treat,
But she cooked it so well you just couldn't tell
The potatoes from the meat—

It was her thing
But she did it wrong.

Well, Johnny's a dazzling skater,
On skates he's as good as they come,
But he fell over so many times one night,
Should have worn skates on his bum—

It was his thing
But he did it wrong.

Now, Frankie is *good* on the cello,
You really should hear Frankie play,
But she played it so badly the audience left
And the cello walked away—

It was her thing
But she did it wrong.

Well, Johnny's a master chess player,
Yes, Johnny's amazing at chess,
But he hit that board so hard with his knee,
Where the pieces were—anyone's guess—

It was his thing
But he did it wrong.

Now, I've written a dim little poem,
I've sung you a boring old song,
Told so many lies, can't believe my eyes,
And I've gone on far too long—

Well, it's my thing
But I've done it wrong!

The Fate of the Supermarket Manager

There once was a Supermarket manager
And a very happy manager was he.

He *reduced the prices*
Of the lollies and the ices!
He made *huge cuts*
On the fruit and nuts!
Corn-flakes, steaks
And home-bake cakes,
Dog-food, detergent,
Devil-fish, dates,
He sold at *half*
The market rates!
And (so my sister
Said to me)
He put stickers
On the knickers
In the Lingerie
Saying:
Prices down
By 15p!
And he wrote, as a treat,
By the luncheon meat:
YOU'D HAVE TO BE BARMY
TO BUY THIS SALAMI
So he gave it away
For free!

Yes, there once was a Supermarket manager
And a very happy manager was he.

What a bloke!

He was much admired.

The shop went broke.

He was fired.

Say Cheese

Cheese!

At Christmas the STILTON
Was spilt on the Wilton,
The rare CAMEMBERT
Was as fine as can be,
But at New Year the GRUYERE
It just went straight through ycr,
The CHEDDAR was bedder
But as for the BRIE,

Aaaaaaaagh! And the PORT SALUD!
Swallow one morsel, you
Kept to your bed
For a week and a day,
And if you tried WENSLEYDALE
You quite *immensely*'d ail,
Hospital-bound
Till they wheeled you away!

No better was EMMENTHAL,
Sour and inclement, all
Cratered and pocked
Like a view of the moon!
And while some are crazy
For creamed BEL PAESE,
Myself, I'd eat forcemeat
Or horsemeat as soon!

The LEICESTER was best o'
The bunch, but the rest o'
Them curled up your stomach.
Though GLOUCESTER (times two)
And jaundiced old CHESHIRE
I'd taste under pressure,
Nothing would get me,
No, nothing would get me,
But nothing would get me
To try DANISH BLUE!

The Frozen Man

Out at the edge of town
where black trees

crack their fingers
in the icy wind

and hedges freeze
on their shadows

and the breath of cattle,
still as boulders,

hangs in rags
under the rolling moon,

a man is walking
alone:

on the coal-black road
his cold

feet
ring

and
ring.

Here in a snug house
at the heart of town

the fire is burning
red and yellow and gold:

you can hear the warmth
like a sleeping cat

breathe softly
in every room.

When the frozen man
comes to the door,

let him in,
let him in,
let him in.

Lies

When we are bored
My friend and I
Tell
Lies.

It's a competition: the prize
Is won by the one
Whose lies
Are the bigger size.

We really do:
That's true.
But there isn't a prize:
That's lies.

Blue Wish

When the gas-fire glows
  It tingles with a
      Low
      Blue light.
      It
Dances with a slow
  Flicker of wishing:
Wish I may,
  Wish I might

Have a blue wish
  Always burning,
Noon,
  Burning,
    Night.

Our Hamster's Life

Our hamster's life:
there's not much
to it,
not much
to it.

He presses his pink nose
to the door of his cage
and decides for the fifty six
millionth time
that he can't get
through it.

Our hamster's life;
there's not much
to it,
not much
to it.

It's about the most boring
life in the world,
if he only
knew it.
He sleeps and he drinks and he eats.
He eats and he drinks and he sleeps.

He slinks and he dreeps.
He eats.

This process
he repeats.

Our hamster's life:
there's not much
to it,
not much
to it.

You'd think it would drive him bonkers,
going round and round on his wheel.
It's certainly driving me bonkers,

watching him
do it.

But he may be thinking:
"That boy's life,
there's not much
to it,
not much
to it:

watching a hamster go round on a wheel.
It's driving me bonkers if he only knew it,

watching him
watching me
do it."

Watch Your French

When my mum tipped a panful of red-hot fat
Over her foot, she did quite a little chat,
And I won't tell you what she said
But it wasn't:
"Fancy that!
I must try in future to be far more careful
With this red-hot scalding fat!"

When my dad fell over and landed—splat!—
With a trayful of drinks (he'd tripped over the cat)
I won't tell you what he said
But it wasn't:
"Fancy that!
I must try in future to be far more careful
To step *round* our splendid cat!"

MON
DIEU!

When Uncle Joe brought me a cowboy hat
Back from the States, the dog stomped it flat,
And I won't tell you what I said
But Mum and Dad yelled:
"STOP THAT!
Where did you learn that appalling language?
Come on. Where?"

"I've no idea," I said,
"No idea."

Bluebells and Penguins

The day we found the lady
Crying in the wood
We tried to comfort her
As best we could
But just what she was crying for
We never understood:

Weeping among the beechleaves and the bluebells.

The day we saw the old man
Cackling at the zoo
We had a laugh along with him
The way you do
But just what he was laughing at
We never had a clue:

Chuckling among the pythons and the penguins!

Now penguins aren't that funny
And bluebells aren't that sad
But sometimes you feel really good
And sometimes you feel bad.
Sometimes you feel sky-high happy,
Sometimes lost and low,
And why on earth you feel like that
Sometimes
     you
       don't
         know!

Jeremy Mobster Lobster

In the black salt-sluices of the weed-choked rockpool
  With fish-eyes, garbage, vanishing fry
And rusting backbones in the squelchy tunnel
  That opens and closes like a murderous eye
  As the tide slurs in and the tide drawls out
  And the grinding shingle churns about,
        With his horrible claws
           For company
        Sits Jeremy Mobster Lobster,
        The meanest fish in the sea.

        The meanest fish,
        The uncleanest fish,
        The obscenest fish in the sea.

Watch out, shrimp! Better say your prayers!
Down in the rockpool
Jeremy's God.
Better have a little bit of
Dead fish ready
For that big mean old
Arth-ro-pod!

Pay up, crayfish! Pay up, crab!
Shell out for Jeremy's
Protection racket.
It'll cost you a packet
But don't complain

Or you might not grow
That shell again . . .

His wavering, wobbly, flickering eye-stalks
  Scrape round the walls of his bony cave
And you'll find no cover in the wallowing darkness,
  You won't be hidden by the blackest wave
For there with the barnacles studding his back
And you in mind as his next big snack,
      With his horrible claws
        For company
    Sits Jeremy Mobster Lobster,
    The meanest fish in the sea.

The meanest fish,
The uncleanest fish,
The obscenest fish in the sea.

All of the Morning

I've been staring
  all of the morning
    out at the endlessly
     falling rain

that drowns the garden
  in tank after tank full
    of see-through tears without
     anger or pain,

joy or sorrow,
  shock or laughter,
    only the helplessly
     falling rain

that springs pink worms
  from their tight dark prison
    and sticks the snails
     to the bumpy wall

with what appear to be
  squiggles of stretched, spat,
    chewed-up chewing-gum.
     Let it fall,

flooding the cones
   of lilac, laburnum's
     yellow bells
       that ring their small

tune of the sun
   in the soaked grey morning,
     let it fall.
       If I weren't me,

the helpless rain
   that falls forever
     I could be,
       quite easily.

Rabbiting Off

Now you see me,
Now you don't,
First you'll miss me,
Then you won't.

Spoken my story,
Sung my song.
I've been round here
All day long

For a yell and a whisper,
Shout and a cough,
Rabbiting on
And sounding off.

Sounding off
And rabbiting on:
I was here
And now I'm . . .

Amy J. Holmes